Darwin and Evolution

From a Catholic Perspective

by
Joseph Bolin

*All booklets are published thanks to the
generous support of the members of the
Catholic Truth Society*

CATHOLIC TRUTH SOCIETY
PUBLISHERS TO THE HOLY SEE

Table of Contents

Acknowledgements: The author would like to thank the readers who gave many helpful comments and suggestions: Michael Bolin, Br Thomas Bolin, James Chastek, Kathleen Holcomb, Jared Kuebler, and Andrew Nuar.

Introduction

Where do I come from? Where am I going? Was I chosen, brought into existence by a loving creator, or am I merely the product of blind chance, of uncaring fate? Few questions are more urgent than these. Men have traditionally sought, and frequently found, answers to these questions in religion. The Judaeo-Christian tradition, indeed, gives a clear answer: God, the benevolent Creator of heaven and earth, brought me into existence by his loving plan. Certain scientists and philosophers have vehemently attacked this answer, loudly proclaiming that human life is a mere happenstance, the product of blind necessity and chance. The militant atheist Richard Dawkins, author of *The Blind Watchmaker* and *The God Delusion*, is among the most well-known figures in this campaign. A prominent battleground in the struggle between "science" and "religion" has been the public schools, with many Christians in favour of teaching "intelligent design" as an alternative to Darwinian evolution, and many scientists strongly opposed to this "unscientific" theory. It has come to the point that we may feel obliged, in spite of ourselves, to take sides and jump into battle: to argue for evolution instead of creation, or creation instead of evolution.

Faith and science

The tension between faith and the scientific theory of evolution is far from new. It began with Darwin himself, who was led to agnosticism partially by his scientific discovery of the origin of species by random variation and natural selection, which took away his confidence in the argument for design proposed by William Paley in his *Natural Theology* (1802). Having no evidence from science for the existence of God, and lacking trust in philosophical arguments for God's existence, his faith was more vulnerable to personal issues such as doubts concerning the doctrine of hell, and the tragedy of his daughter Annie's death.[1]

The tension grew as certain proponents of evolution engaged in polemics against the Church. Thomas Huxley argued that "the books of ecclesiastical authority" were contrary to science, and that the position of Christian theologians was "hopelessly untenable." John Tyndall argued that prayers for the alleviation of poor harvests or cattle plague were an obstacle to progress, discouraging study of the real causes of scarcity and disease.[2] Many churchmen reacted defensively to such polemics, and were suspicious of the increasingly secular scientific outlook and the claims of evolution.

Although scientists took some time to accept natural selection as a principal moving force of evolution, they tended overall to see Darwin's theory as confirmed by the evidence. The sticking point for many Christians was the acceptance of human evolution, as they were not sure how to reconcile it with the account in the first chapter of Genesis. Many, although ready to accept evolution in general, were unwilling to accept it as regards the human body. This way of thinking, as the evidence for evolution continued to grow, resulted at times in a kind of double thinking; scientific evidence would be accepted, but only as long as it didn't impinge on the view that man was miraculously formed from the earth.

Intelligent design movement

The evidence for evolution continued to increase, and certain proponents of evolution became more vocal in arguing that evolution takes place by ruthless laws and blind, unguided chance, and excludes any place for God in the world. In response, a movement formed that attempted to "save" God's role in the formation of the world, by finding scientific evidence for "intelligent design."[3] The majority of scientists considered the arguments and positions of this movement to be quite unscientific, which added to the apparent tension between the scientific view of evolution and the Judaeo-Christian religious view of an intelligent, loving creator.

Christoph Cardinal Schönborn, the archbishop of Vienna, entered the dispute with an essay published on the editorial page of the New York Times, titled "Finding Design in Nature" (7th July, 2005). In it he granted the possibility of evolution in the sense of common ancestry, but strongly rejected evolution in the neo-Darwinian sense of "an unguided, unplanned process of random variation and natural selection," insisting that "any system of thought that denies or seeks to explain away the overwhelming evidence for design in biology is ideology, not science." His essay was widely taken as expressing support for the intelligent design movement. The Cardinal's primary intention, however, was quite different. He desired to raise the discussion to a philosophical level; his primary contention was not that the *science* regarding evolution was wrong, but that neo-Darwinians who claim natural selection and random genetic variation as evidence of an absolutely unguided evolutionary process are advancing beyond science to materialist ideology. In a series of talks and essays, later published in book form as *Chance or Purpose?: Creation, Evolution, and a Rational Faith*,[4] Cardinal Schönborn worked through various philosophical and theological issues raised by evolution.

The goal of this work is to clarify and present in a simple manner the relationship between Darwin's theory of evolution and Catholic doctrine, particularly the doctrine of creation, and to show how they are not only compatible but also complementary. Being connected with human origins, evolution in fact touches upon not only questions of creation, but also questions of natural law, ethics, the relation of man and woman, grace, original sin, etc. Still, creation is the most fundamental of these questions, and understanding the compatibility of evolution and creation is crucial for dealing with many of the other issues raised by evolution. Natural law and ethics follow from man's rational nature, which makes him capable of knowing objective truth and living according to it. The supernatural vocation to grace flows from the same loving plan of God who creates human beings out of love. Due to the key importance of creation in understanding evolution, and in the interest of brevity, we will mostly limit ourselves to considering the relationship of evolution and creation.

Creation

As in many other matters, the Catholic understanding of creation is truly *catholic*, that is, universal, while other understandings of creation are limited. We will examine four of these forms of "creationism": six-day creationism, progressive creationism, deistic creationism, and intelligent design creationism. When we have grasped the limitations of these approaches, it will be easier to appreciate the Catholic doctrine.

Four Understandings of Creation

Six-day Creationism
(Literal and Simplistic Interpretation)

The first kind of creationism is based on a very literal reading of Genesis, taking the "six days" of Genesis as physical days, and indeed days of the same length as ours, 24 hours. According to this understanding of creation, God formed all basic kinds of living beings directly. No kind descended from another, but all were created separately by God.

This form of creationism is not based on experimental science, but on a particular reading of Scripture. Those who advance this view do not believe that the sun, the earth, and all plants and animals were formed in six days based on observable and scientific evidence. Rather, they believe this because they believe in the infallible truth of Scripture, and they think Scripture asserts that the entire world was formed in six days. Robert Sungenis, a proponent of six-day creationism, puts the argument plainly: "The only absolute certainty we have in this world is what comes from the mouth of God. In His word it states that He created the universe in six days, not six billion years or sixteen billion years."[5] He does not claim that science *proves* creation in six days, but that it does not *disprove* it: "As for science, the facts are plain: we have found no irrefutable scientific evidence to deny this divine revelation."[6]

Leaving aside the shaky claim about the lack of scientific proof for a longer duration of the earth's formation, purely exegetical arguments can be advanced against this interpretation of Genesis. Three examples of such arguments:

- The first verses of Genesis describe a formless earth *before* the first day, which begins, like the other days of creation, with "and God said," whereas, if the "days" described a temporal or historical order, nothing could be before the first day.

- The diverse sequences of creation in Genesis 1, Genesis 2, and Job 38:4-7 suggest that the texts do not

intend to present a historical order, but to illustrate
God's work of creation in one or another aspect.

- Genesis 2:5, which explains that no plant was in the earth
  because God had not caused it to rain upon the earth,
  shows that creation followed the ordinary laws of God's
  providence. But if Genesis 1 is understood in a
  chronological order, then plants were created before the
  sun was created, which is incompatible with the principle
  of God's providence - since plants require the sun.[7]

Progressive Creationism

The second kind of creationism, progressive creationism,
maintains that God created new forms of life
progressively, by distinct acts of creation. In this view,
the progression from simple forms to more complex
forms of life is not the result of evolution, but the result
of God's repeated intervention in the world. The basis for
this view may be (1) philosophical, (2) theological, (3)
empirical, or a combination of these. (1) According to a
certain philosophical view of *substance*, or *nature*, it is
impossible for one kind of living being to generate
another. According to this view, reproduction always
stays within the same species. So if cats and dogs are
different species, they cannot be descended from a
common ancestor, since then some animal must have
generated an animal different from itself in species. (2) A

related theological basis for this view of creationism is a particular reading of Genesis 1, "God created the great sea monsters and every living creature that moves... according to their kinds... and every winged bird according to its kind... the beasts of the earth according to their kinds," or Genesis 2:19, "Out of the ground the LORD God formed every beast of the field and every bird of the air." One might interpret these texts to mean that each particular kind of animal was *directly* created or formed by God, even if, as the fossil record indicates, all kinds of animals were not formed *simultaneously*. (3) One might affirm progressive creationism on the basis of empirical evidence: if one thinks that science shows that it is impossible for all living beings to have arisen by reproduction with modifications, or evolution, then one must postulate some interventions in the process of reproduction/evolution, interventions that bring about new kinds of living beings.

Deistic Creationism

Deism, and deistic creationism, is largely the fruit of empirical Enlightenment philosophy. Though there are different types of deism, a common theme is the rejection of God's supernatural intervention in the world or supernatural revelation. Deistic creationism as we understand it here is the belief that God made the world, but has no more influence on it. It sees God's creative activity only in the very beginning of things, establishing the laws of the universe and its original state. It as though God made a great machine, wound it up, and then left it to run on its own.

Some deistic creationists, following a very fundamentalist/literalistic interpretation of Scripture, hold that God created living beings in the beginning, but that these living beings then developed completely on their own. Other deistic creationists hold that God created only the matter of the universe and its laws of physics, and that the development and formation of the world followed from these laws. Since deistic creationists generally accept recognised scientific theses, which propose a gradual development of living beings, this latter form of deistic creationism is the most common one.

Intelligent Design Creationism

Intelligent design creationism is the view that God created the world by "designing" certain structures within it, either at the beginning, or at multiple points in its development. Properly speaking, the theory of intelligent design is not a theory of creation, and does not presuppose a divine creator. It is rather a scientific, or pseudo-scientific, theory that the structure of the world or of living beings shows the working of an intelligent designer. Yet while this designer could theoretically be some finite intelligent agent, such as intelligent extraterrestrials, most adherents of the theory of intelligent design understand

God to be the designer. Consequently, intelligent design theory is often associated with creationism.

The popular origins of the term "intelligent design" also demonstrate a link with creationism. The biology textbook *Of Pandas and People* has been said to be the first to use the phrase "intelligent design" in its present sense,[8] and was certainly the first to use the phrase extensively. Early drafts of this book spoke frequently of creation, defining it as meaning that "the various forms of life began abruptly through the agency of an intelligent creator with their distinctive features already intact. Fish with fins and scales, birds with feathers, beaks, and wings, etc." It followed what we have called progressive creationism, though allowing for the possibility of a more rapid creation, such as creation in six days. After the USA Supreme Court in *Edwards v. Aguillard* ruled it unconstitutional to teach creation science in public schools, the book's authors systematically replaced terms such as "creator" with "intelligent designer." The previous definition of "creation" was preserved, but was now used as a definition of "intelligent design"![9]

Michael Behe

Two principal arguments are made for intelligent design: one based on *complexity*, the other based on *information*. These arguments for intelligent design may be seen in the work of two key proponents of the theory, Michael Behe and William Dembski. Behe, a practicing Catholic and microbiologist, was for a long time a Darwinist who saw no theological or scientific problems with the theory of the common descent of living beings by a process of random change and natural selection. That changed abruptly when he read the geneticist Michael Denton's *Evolution: A Theory in Crisis*. He describes the experience as world-changing: "When I laid the book down, I lived in a different world."[10] He began reading with a skeptical eye the claims for evolution in the scientific literature, and volunteered to lead a seminar titled "Popular Arguments on Evolution," in which he and his students read and discussed pro- and anti-evolution books and articles, particularly Denton's *Evolution: A Theory in Crisis* and Richard Dawkin's *The Blind Watchmaker*. The next stage in his engagement with the theory of evolution came when he read the lawyer Phillip Johnson's book *Darwin on Trial*, which argued that if one did not assume materialism was true, then the evidence for random mutation and natural selection as the explanation of life on earth is very small indeed.[11] In the following months Behe became involved in debates on evolution with Phillip Johnson, and worked out the arguments that later became the basis for his own book *Darwin's Black Box*,[12] arguments that he believed made a unique contribution from the perspective of biochemistry.

Behe's complexity

The key concept in Behe's argument is *irreducible complexity*. The argument begins with two premises: (1) certain parts of organisms, such as the mechanism for blood clotting, or the bacterial flagellum, are *complex*, that is, they are composed of many different parts; (2) *all* of these parts are necessary in order to achieve the function; in other words, the mechanism is *irreducibly* complex; the structure cannot be simpler and have the same function. The second step of the argument is that such an irreducibly complex mechanism cannot be built up gradually, by a process of natural selection. If the mechanism producing the function is irreducibly complex, then intermediate structures would have no function, and thus no value for the organism; they would not contribute to its living or reproducing, and so would not be promoted by natural selection.

The concept of irreducible complexity as an objection to evolution by natural selection is not really new. Darwin himself recognised it: "If it could be demonstrated that any complex organ existed which could not possibly have been formed by numerous, successive, slight modifications, my theory would absolutely break down."[13] Behe's contribution was the application of this idea at the molecular level rather than at the level of large organs such as the eye. Complex bio-chemical processes are supposed to exemplify exactly such a complexity as Darwin spoke of. Behe proclaimed that design is clearly evident at the cellular level, and that this discovery "must be ranked as one of the greatest achievements in the history of science," rivaling those of Newton, Einstein, Lavoisier, Schrödinger, Pasteur, and Darwin.[14]

Application of complexity

While the general principle is sound, its application is weak. A "molecular machine" that requires each of its parts in order to perform its function could have been built up from parts with different functions. Indeed, this is just what the theory of evolution would predict! As the ancestors of horses were not simply "imperfect horses," but were something other than horses, so one could expect the precursor of many biological systems to be not merely imperfect systems of the same type, but systems functioning somewhat differently.

More generally, the argument that some biological system could not have been formed gradually is an argument based on ignorance: we don't know how, or at least don't know *exactly* how such-and-such a function evolved; therefore, it couldn't have evolved gradually. This argument is weak, unless we suppose that we know biochemistry so well that if there *were* a gradual way for the function to evolve, we would know it. Since our knowledge of biochemistry remains quite imperfect regarding many detailed points, the fact that we do not know *in detail* how gradual evolution of various functional systems could have happened is a weak argument that it is impossible. But in fact, possible paths of evolution have been sketched out for the very things, such as blood clotting, that Behe claims are *irreducibly complex*![15]

Dembski's probability theory

William Dembski, a mathematician and philosopher, attempted to give a rigorous, quasi-mathematical foundation for the theory of intelligent design. In his technical book *The Design Inference*, revised from his Ph.D. dissertation in philosophy and published by Cambridge University Press in a series on probability theory, he proposes the three categories of law, chance, or design. If an event is regular and necessary (or highly probable), then it is the result of *law*. If an event has an intermediate probability, or if it has a very low probability but is not a particularly special event, then it is the result of *chance*. If an event has a very low probability, and matches an independently given specification, then it is the result of *design*. To describe low probability together with an independent specification, Dembski uses the term *specified complexity*, or *complex specified information*. Dembski was by no means the first to use the notion of specified complexity. Richard Dawkins himself, explaining why animals seem designed, employed the same concept: "complicated things have some quality, specifiable in advance, that is highly unlikely to have been acquired by random chance alone."[16] Dembski's innovation is his attempt to use this notion of complexity to exclude origination through law and chance. In this original work, *The Design Inference*, Dembski did not apply the principle to natural organisms and events, but in later writings he sought to apply the *design inference* to nature.

There are several weaknesses in Dembski's argument. Simply showing that a large *quantity* of information or complexity is present is insufficient, since complexity can be produced by chance. (An attempt to memorise random series of numbers quickly shows that randomness and complexity go together.) Even showing that the complexity somehow fits an independent pattern is insufficient, since chance together with law can do this. A computer can take random input and transform it by a regular method, or law, so that the result is unique, or highly complex, on account of the randomness involved, and also highly specified, on account of the regularity involved. Examples of this are solutions to problems that are found by the use of computer genetic algorithms, or unique music that is written by computers. In some cases, computers have even found better solutions to problems than humans have. Dr. Adrian Thompson, for example, by means of a genetic algorithm evolved a device that could distinguish between the words "go" and "stop," using only 37 logic gates - far fewer than a human engineer would need to solve the problem.[17] And while computer-generated music may not yet be great music, it is certainly not mere noise. According to any *purely mathematical* definition of information, such programs *can* produce information.[18]

In order for Dembski to apply the design inference to nature, he needs to exclude such a combination of chance and law, to exclude the possibility of information in the sense of *new possibilities* being introduced by chance, and becoming *specified* information by the regular process of natural selection (organisms are matched to their environment by the greater reproduction of those which match it). The only way he can do this is to fall back on Behe's notion of irreducible complexity.[19] That is, he has to posit, implicitly or explicitly, that the specified information must be introduced in one fell swoop; thus it cannot be attributed to chance, since the probabilities are far too small, nor can it be attributed to law, since there is no set law to produce it. Dembski begins his argument with a different concept than Behe does, namely that of "information," but when it comes to applying the argument to real biological systems, Dembski's argument more or less coincides with Behe's.

Intelligent Design and Common Descent

The theory of intelligent design does not necessarily mean rejection or doubt regarding the common descent or ancestry of living beings. Michael Behe, for instance, states his belief that "the evidence strongly supports common descent,"[20] and that he disputes not the fact of common descent, but the process of natural selection.[21] Nevertheless, there is a strong connection between the theory of intelligent design and doubts regarding common descent, and many people who support the theory of intelligent design do question the fact of common descent. Why? Well, if the "information" or structure of an organism has to be *immediately* attributed to the designer, and cannot arise through a process of chance and natural selection, then this designer must have either (1) put all the information for all species into the first living cell, or (2) suddenly inserted the information or complex structures at certain points of natural history. The first option is implausible. If the DNA for eyes, ears, heart, human brain, etc., was all somehow present in the first living cell, why was it preserved for so long during its inactive period, rather than being gradually obliterated by mutations? We would have to posit not only a special work of the designer at the beginning, but a special providence that preserved organisms from mutations that would destroy the DNA needed for the future development of species. While the second option, that the designer inserted information or formed structures all at once, is more plausible, it also raises philosophical or theological questions. One has to ask, if the designer inserted new structures in the offspring of existing organisms, why didn't the designer simply form entirely new organisms, rather than altering existing ones? Why did the designer alter the organisms in such a way, and at such times, that they show a familial resemblance, that they look as though they were produced in a natural manner, by reproduction? Why did the designer produce so many forms that were just going to become extinct, without descendants?

Scientists' reaction to Intelligent Design

Since common descent is considered by the mainstream scientific community to be as certain as any other scientific fact, the rejection or serious questioning of common descent by many proponents of intelligent design makes it hard for the scientific community to take them seriously. Moreover, proponents of intelligent design write few peer-reviewed scientific articles, instead publishing books, and often appealing to a more popular audience. Some are accused of quoting scientists out of context in order to borrow support for their views. Behe, for example, in the section of his book that calls neo-Darwinism into question, quotes Jerry Coyne as saying, "We conclude - unexpectedly - that there is little evidence for the neo-Darwinian view: its theoretical foundations and the experimental evidence supporting it are weak."[22] As quoted by Behe, Coyne seemed to be expressing doubt about neo-Darwinian evolution in general. Behe had omitted the final clause of the sentence, which was "...and there is no doubt that mutations of large effect are sometimes important in adaptation." Coyne responded with a complaint that Behe had twisted his words by citing them out of context, and citing only part of a sentence. "In the middle of our sentence, Behe found a period that wasn't there."[23] The paper that Behe cited was concerned with the question whether mutations of large effect might sometimes be important, and spoke of the neo-Darwinian view as the view that adaptations are based on many *small* genetic mutations. Coyne's paper, co-authored with Allen Orr, came to the conclusion that mutations with a large effect are sometimes important. "By inserting the period (and removing the sentence from its neighbours), Behe has twisted our meaning. Our discussion of one aspect of Darwinism - the relative size of adaptive mutations - has suddenly become a critique of the entire Darwinian enterprise. This is not sloppy scholarship, but deliberate distortion."[24]

Intelligent Design and Philosophy

Cardinal Schönborn, often thought to be on the side of the intelligent design school of thought, sees a fundamental failure in its quasi-scientific attempt to see complexity in nature as proof of a designer, because design or purpose "cannot be found on the level of causality with which the scientific method is concerned." The limitations of the scientific method do not allow it either to prove or to disprove an intelligent origin and purpose of the world.[25]

Indeed, while the theory of intelligent design is sometimes seen as the best alternative to radical neo-Darwinism, the two theories actually share deep roots in common. Both theories arose in the *milieu* born of nominalism and scientism, and try to answer the questions about the origin of life without substantial reference to philosophy. They abstract from the notions of *nature*, *substantial form*, and *intrinsic purpose*, and share a mechanistic view of living beings: while the theory of intelligent design claims that a complicated mechanism must be formed by a designer, Darwinism claims that a mechanism, consisting essentially of various parts and based on various genes, can arise gradually. Both theories suppose a false opposition between law and design, in contrast to classical philosophy, which sees design (i.e., the work of intelligence) in *every* natural law. Though the scientific claim of intelligent design - that known natural causes could not produce the life we see - must finally be judged on its scientific merit, on how well it corresponds to the evidence, the philosophical mindset underlying this understanding of intelligent design is highly questionable.

A positive fruit of intelligent design creationism is that it has raised public debate about the legitimate claims of science, and the relation of philosophy and science. On the other hand, due to the scientifically dubious arguments made by proponents of intelligent design, it has also led to suspicions that support of intelligent design comes merely from Christian bias, and that faith and science really are opposed, despite the claims of the Catholic Church to the contrary.

Limitation of These Understandings of Creation

All of these interpretations of creation share a common weakness or limitation. They see God's creative action as restricted either to the beginning, or to certain moments when God intervenes in the world, rather than seeing God's creative action as pervading the entire world at all times, which is the genuine Catholic understanding. For a variety of reasons, especially the pervasiveness of scientism, such restrictive interpretations of creation have come to predominate, and the Catholic understanding of creation has faded somewhat into the background. In the following section we will examine this full Catholic understanding.

Catholic Understanding of Creation

Fathers of the Church

Why is it important to study the Church Fathers? Not because they know more than we do in every respect and in every field, but because they are nearer to the original revelation made through Christ and the apostles. We do not take the Fathers as teachers in medicine, biology, natural history, etc., but as interpreters of Scripture and of Divine Revelation. So how do the Fathers understand the revealed account of the creation of the world? What is the meaning of the account in Genesis?

There are many things we could look at in the Fathers, but we will focus on their interpretations of the nature and order of the "days" of creation. Regarding the *duration* of creation, the Church Fathers do not unanimously insist on interpreting the days as signifying intervals of 24 hours. Some are open to these other interpretations, and others are positively in favour of other interpretations. Origen takes up the objection that the Genesis account of creation on certain days is ridiculous, since days did not exist before the heavens and the earth were made, nor was the sun rising and setting. In response to this objection, he criticises those who, "taking the words in their apparent signification, said that the time of six days was occupied in the creation of the world." He rejects the interpretation of the six days as six consecutive intervals, though he does not offer his own alternative interpretation. He is content to see a mystery in the order of the days, without seeking to explain the actual historical sequence: "Who that has understanding will suppose that the first and second and third day existed without a sun and moon and stars and that the first day was, as it were, also without a sky?... I do not suppose that anyone doubts that these things figuratively indicate certain mysteries, the history having taken place in appearance and not literally."[26]

St Justin Martyr and Irenaeus understand the "day" in which Adam is told, "the day that you eat" of the fruit of knowledge of good and evil "you shall die" (*Gn* 2:17), to refer to a thousand years.[27] Both cite the text, "The day of the Lord is as a thousand years" (2 *P* 3:8). It has been argued that several Fathers apply this understanding to the six days of creation, taking them as six thousand years.[28]

Theophilus of Antioch gives a noteworthy explanation of the account in Genesis: plants and seeds came into existence before the stars, in order to show the error of philosophers who assert that the stars produced the things on earth.[29] In other words, the intention of the text is to make clear that *God* is the author both of the things in the heavens and of the things on the earth. While Theophilus appears to believe that this is also the historical order, he sees the primary intent of the text not as historical, but as showing God's primacy in the work of creation.

St Augustine also understands the days figuratively, referring them to angels' knowledge of creation rather than the historical creation, or referring "night" to the changeability of things, and "day" to their formation, rather than to the passage of time.[30]

Summarising these and other Fathers of the Church, there are three basic ways of reading the days of creation: (1) the *24-hour view*, in which the six days of creation are historically sequential, 24-hour days; (2) the *day-age view*, in which the six days are historically sequential, longer periods of time, e.g., a thousand years, represented by "days"; (3) the *framework view*, in which the six days are figurative, arranged not in historical order, but in another manner: e.g., descending from general to particular, from the basic stuff of the world to the things that fill it. We cannot immediately exclude any of these three readings simply on the basis of the authority of the Fathers of the Church. While they themselves have various interpretations, they do not all insist upon one particular interpretation as contained in divine tradition.

The positive divine teaching about creation that the Fathers see in Scripture is that: (1) God is not dependent on something outside himself, but is the source of everything in the world; (2) God created the world from nothing.

St Augustine

Since creation does *not* mean merely that God formed preexisting matter, but that he is the cause of everything that exists, creation does not exclude the involvement of creaturely causality. St Augustine seems to have affirmed a kind of evolution, though he does not go into detail: God imparted fundamental powers to the nature of things, which in due time gave rise to the different species of plants and animals.[31]

St Augustine has strong words regarding the intention of the divine author of Genesis, and the folly of interpreting Scripture in a manner contrary to sound science. He notes that many things about the world may be known "with the greatest certainty" by non-Christians, and that if Christians have false opinions about these matters, opinions that they seem to get from the Scriptures, they subject the faith to ridicule.

It not infrequently happens that something about the earth, about the sky, about other elements of this world... about the nature of animals, of fruits, of stones, and of other such things, may be known with the greatest certainty by reasoning or by experience, even by one who is not a Christian. It is too disgraceful and ruinous, and greatly to be avoided, that he [the non-Christian] should hear a Christian speaking so idiotically on these matters, and as if in accord with Christian writings, that he might say that he could scarcely keep from laughing when he saw how totally in error they are.[32]

St Augustine draws the logical conclusion: when experience and science clearly point to some fact about the world, we should not interpret the Scriptures as affirming the contrary. The aim of the Scriptures is to treat of the faith, and so apparent assertions about the world that are contrary to fact should not be read as assertions at all.

"With the Scriptures it is a matter of treating about the faith. For that reason... [if anyone] should find something about these matters [concerning the physical universe] in our books... [which] seems to be at variance with the perceptions of his own rational faculties, let him believe that these things are in no way necessary to the admonitions or accounts or predictions of the Scriptures."[33]

This hermeneutic principle of St Augustine is important. While the divine knowledge given us by Scripture is in its own right more sure than any human knowledge, our certainty about the *meaning* of Scripture may be much less than the certainty of some human science. In that case we should not contradict the relative certainty of human science with our very fallible interpretation of Scripture. Sungenis, reading Genesis in a literalistic way, and therefore asserting that the world and all forms of life were made in six days, despite massive scientific evidence to the contrary, seems to have erred by neglecting this Augustinian principle of interpretation.

Thomas Aquinas

St Thomas Aquinas gives precise formulation to the scriptural and patristic teaching: to call God the Creator means that all "being" comes from him,[34] that is, the existence of anything whatsoever comes from God, and depends essentially upon him. "Being" here includes *being active*, and so the activity and power of everything derives from God's creative action.

St Thomas sees the power of God's creative action not only in making things *exist*, but above all in making them be *causes* of other things. The production of one creature by another does not compete with God's causality, as though a creature had to be either from God *or* from another creature. Rather, whatever is produced by a creature comes from God as the first and ultimate cause of it, and from the creature as a secondary cause. (We are speaking, of course, about *real beings* that are produced; sin, as a moral defect and privation, is not from God.) Since God is the cause of all other causes, his causality includes even chance events, which occur by the coincidence of two causes.[35]

St Thomas sees the ability of one natural being to be generated by another natural being as rooted in "first matter," the radical possibility of a material being to become one thing or another. When a natural agent forms a structure suited for the living activities of growth, etc., the result is not merely a complex structure, like a machine, but really becomes a living being. Yet while matter is necessary for this change, the change itself cannot be attributed only to the matter, which is merely the inner root of the *possibility* of being a living being; the change must ultimately be attributed to the cause of matter, which is God. This is true not only of the human soul, which in a certain manner transcends material reality, but of every nature, which *is* something more than the *stuff* in which it is found. The existence of a natural being cannot be attributed only to that which materially formed it, but must also be attributed to the author of nature.

Aquinas' empiricism

Since created things receive from God not only existence, but also the power to be causes of other things, Thomas's view of creation leaves room for a natural sequence such as evolution in the created world, whereby one type of living being comes from another. We cannot determine *a priori* the extent to which this can or does happen concretely. We cannot say *a priori*, for example, that a living being can only produce something essentially like itself, but can only make a judgment about this on the basis of experience. St Thomas, in fact, following Aristotle and the common scientific opinion, held that simpler living beings are generated by the powers of the heavens (we might say, by "natural forces") acting upon inanimate substances, while more complex living beings are generated by other living beings like them in kind. He believed this not for purely theoretical reasons, but because he saw it as the best account given the data available. This particular account of abiogenesis ("spontaneous generation") has been falsified, at least as regards the living beings we see commonly around us. But the general possibility of life being generated through natural forces remains open, as does the possibility of one kind of organism generating another kind. It is the task of empirical science to determine whether, when, and how this actually happens.

Magisterium on Creation

In this section we examine the Church's understanding of what it means for God to create. Church statements pertaining to the particular order and duration of creation will be considered later, in the section on creation and evolution.

The Church has always taught that everything was created by God, as expressed in its creeds, "I believe in God... the Creator of heaven and earth," where heaven and earth stand for all spiritual and material reality. Lateran Council IV taught that God created all creatures from nothing, by his omnipotent power. Vatican I taught that God created not out of necessity, but out of his goodness, by a free and knowing plan. In addition, it affirmed the possibility of knowing God with certainty from the consideration of created things.[36]

Creation is the production of things "from nothing," inasmuch as God does not depend on anything in order to create. Creation means not only bringing things into being, but also upholding them in being. Creation is not just a single event in the beginning, but is *continuous*, since God continuously upholds all things in being.[37]

Again, creation is the production of things "according to their whole substance." God is not only the cause of hydrogen's existence, but also of its nature, with all its properties and powers. Whatever hydrogen does, whatever light does, whatever anything created does, is ultimately dependent on God's creative causality. God's active involvement in all actions of creatures is inseparable from the Catholic doctrine of creation. God is the first cause, who acts in and through secondary causes.[38] But while God works through and in his creation, certain effects surpass the power of created causes, and are properly attributed to God alone. For example, though human parents give life to their children, they do not make human *souls*, which are created by God alone.[39]

We can summarise the chief points regarding creation under three heads:

- God is the cause of everything that is: he brought things into being in the beginning, and constantly upholds them in being.

- God creates freely, out of love, with a wise and intelligent plan.

- God is active in everything that acts; their action presupposes his action.

Concluding summary

When as Catholics we profess our faith, "I believe in God the Father Almighty, the Creator of heaven and earth," we affirm our belief that all things whatsoever, great and small, tangible and intangible, visible and invisible, receive their existence from God, who, with an intelligent and loving plan, brought them into existence and preserves them in existence. Because God is the cause of everything in the world, he is quite unlike the causes we see around us. I can stretch a plant by pulling on it, but cannot make it *grow*. I can make changes in it, but these are not *natural* changes. God, on the other hand, being the cause of the plant's very life and of all the stuff (chemicals, atoms, and so on) of which it is made, causes the plant to grow upwards naturally. All the natural activities and changes in the world presuppose and depend on God's creative action.

Darwinian Evolution

In order to understand evolution correctly, we must understand (1) what the theory of evolution as a scientific theory encompasses, and (2) the limitations of scientific method.

With regard to the scientific view of evolution, we have to distinguish the *theory* or *theories* of evolution from the *fact* of evolution. The fact of evolution refers to the historical origin of living organisms by way of descent with modifications from common ancestors. This includes both what is sometimes termed "microevolution" (small modifications within a basic kind of living being) and "macroevolution" (changes from one kind or species of living being to another). It is considered a fact because the evidence in its favour is so strong that "no knowledgeable and unbiased person could deny its reality."[40] Like the proposition that the sun is at the center of our planetary system, evolution began as an hypothesis, but came to be acknowledged as a fact as the evidence for it became overwhelming.[41] In contrast, the view of natural selection and random mutation as the principal cause of evolution remains a *theory* that seeks to explain evolution as a *fact*. A few scientists hold other theories of evolution, in which natural selection would play a less substantial role, and other principles a greater role. The renowned paleontologist Simon Conway Morris, for example, arguing from convergent evolution (i.e., the fact that similar biological systems, such as the eye, have evolved independently multiple times), claims there must be "laws" of evolution that direct into predetermined pathways.

Science and reality:
the limitations of the scientific method

Modern science considers primarily those causes that are most accessible to the senses, namely the *stuff* of which things are made, and the way that they *interact*, what the scholastics called material and efficient causes. Questions about what the scholastics called formal or final causes - the inner essence of things, and their final purpose - are methodically ignored by science.

Moreover, modern science considers material things and their interactions only insofar as material things and their interactions can be measured and described in a way that may be verified or falsified by precisely defined sensible evidence or tests. When science considers two magnets that move towards each other, it does not consider the real *cause* of this motion. It does not consider, for example, whether each is moving itself, or each is moving the other. Instead, it considers the motion only insofar as it is possible to give a description of *when* and *how* motion occurs, a description that may be verified or falsified by sensible experience.

Science's methodological restriction to those aspects of reality that can be verified or falsified by precisely defined experiments enables it to have remarkable success, but also means that science cannot *directly* make claims about the nature of things, their purpose, or even the nature of the very causes it considers. To understand the ultimate significance of scientific claims, science must be interpreted in light of a more fundamental, ultimately *philosophical* understanding of the world. This can happen for better or for worse: science interpreted by good philosophy leads to a *greater understanding* of reality; science interpreted by bad philosophy leads to a *misunderstanding* of reality.

Materialistic interpretation of science

The interpretation of scientific conclusions through the lens of materialism is a common mistake that may sometimes slip in unnoticed. The scientist *methodologically* focuses on material and efficient causes, but may unwittingly extend this methodological reductionism to a *philosophical* reductionism, an assertion about the real world. A biochemist studying an animal methodologically restricts his study to the elements of the animal and the interactions among these elements. If he observes that living functions such as digestion, sight, locomotion, and so on, arise from the interactions of the various components in the animal, he may be tempted to conclude that science has "proven" that animals are nothing more than a bundle of chemicals interacting with each other. *This* assertion, about the very nature of animals, is a philosophical assertion, which cannot rightly be deduced from any scientific conclusion of the chemist, except on the presupposition of *another* philosophical premise, that a thing *is* nothing more than the stuff of which it is made. Science does not prove the validity of materialism, except on the presupposition of materialism - a circular argument, but one which is hidden by the fact that a scientist originally assumes only a kind of methodological materialism, which he then without notice extends to philosophical materialism.

Similarly a biologist studying the evolution of animals finds that animals with sight came from animals without sight, that men came from irrational animals, that animals in general probably came from non-sensate living beings, and so may be tempted to conclude that "sight" is an illusion (that is, that animals with sight react to light just as a security camera may react to what it "sees," but without really seeing), and that men are not essentially different from or superior to animals, nor animals essentially different from plants. This conclusion might seem to be justified by the philosophical principle that an effect cannot be greater than its causes. But in fact, the conclusion does not follow from this principle, except on the supposition of *another* principle, namely that there is no agent outside material reality, an agent that could cause a greater nature in man than man's "ancestors" possessed, or a greater nature in sensate living beings than their ancestors possessed. Philosophical materialism sneaks in the back door of the so-called "scientific" argument for materialistic evolution.

Evolution and Philosophy

In order to avoid such errors in interpreting the scientific fact of evolution, we need an adequate natural philosophy, a philosophy that has a place for nature and intrinsic purpose, as complements of matter and external agencies. The fact that an animal is composed of atoms (its matter) does not mean that it is not really *one* thing, with *one* nature; similarly the fact that an animal was derived from another kind of animal, with different activities and a different purpose, does not mean that it does not have its *own* activity and purpose. How do we know that our eyes are for seeing, ears for hearing, our nose for smelling, our mouth for eating? It is not because we believe that they were created by someone who intended these things. We know that our eyes are for seeing because our eyes *can* see, and because seeing contributes to our *good*. How the eye came to be is not really relevant to this question. If an organ capable of seeing came to be from an organ that was not capable of seeing, that does not show that the organ capable of sight does not exist for the sake of sight - it shows only that there was some kind of material continuity or similarity between the organ which was not for the sake of seeing, and the organ which is for the sake of seeing.

To summarise, the scientific fact and theory of evolution must be carefully interpreted in light of sound philosophy, in order to avoid a too narrow vision of the facts of evolution, and to avoid treating a partial truth as though it were the entire truth.

Creation and Evolution

The International Theological Commission's document, *Communion and Stewardship*, considering the relation of faith and science, notes that "Christians have the responsibility to locate the modern scientific understanding of the universe within the context of the theology of creation."[42] This modern scientific understanding of the universe includes evolution. Despite the polemics surrounding the issue, evolution correctly understood, and creation in the Catholic sense, are quite compatible.

Magisterium on evolution

From the first publication of Darwin's *Origin of Species*, the Church has in principle had an open ear to what natural history and science may discern regarding the formation of the world, though with caution as pertains to man's origin and nature. Some Catholics saw no especial difficulty with the theory of evolution. A theologian of the stature of John Henry Newman thought nothing more sensible than evolution as an explanation of the similarities among animals, and between men and monkeys: "There is as much want of simplicity in the

44

idea of the creation of distinct species as in that of the creation of trees in full growth, or of rocks with fossils in them. I mean that it is as strange that monkeys should be so like men, with no historical connexion between them, as [that there should be] no history of facts by which fossil bones got into rocks."[43] Others saw more difficulty in the theory, questioning whether the theory that the human body arose by evolution was compatible with divine revelation. Some wanted the Church to condemn the opinion that the first man's body was formed by a process of evolution, but the Church refrained from making any such declaration.[44]

Censorship

In some cases the Congregation of the Index of Forbidden Books took action to end publication of books favouring evolution. The Congregation asked two authors, Dalmace Leroy and John Zahm, to cease publishing their books that advocated the theory. Leroy agreed to publicly retract his position, while the Congregation did not ask this of Zahm, who only wrote privately to his publisher to cease publication of the book.[45] These decisions were not from the Holy Office (the Supreme Tribunal of the Holy See), but only from the Congregation of the Index, and thus did not carry dogmatic authority.[46] Moreover, the reason for the decision was not given, and it could have been merely a prudential one, that it was potentially scandalous to affirm such positions. The decisions were deliberately not published, but communicated privately to the authors, seemingly because the Congregation did not want to take a public stance on the issue. The only book actually placed on the Index of Forbidden Books for its defense of evolution was Raffaello Caverni's book proposing the reconciliation of evolution with Catholic doctrine.[47]

In other cases the Congregation took no action. George Mivart, a Catholic biologist, published a book *On the Genesis of Species* in 1871. In this book he accepted evolution, though arguing against the central role that Darwin had assigned to natural selection. Moreover, he notes how some theologians bring forth quite inaccurate critiques of Darwinism, and attributes this in part to the logical reaction of believers to the attacks that a number of evolutionists had made against theology. He observes that creation and evolution are not opposed, and many Christian thinkers accept both of them. Distinguishing creation in an absolute sense, as the origin of something out of nothing, and in a secondary sense, as the formation of something out of the powers that God put into creation, he argues that the apparent opposition between creation and evolution comes from confusing these senses of creation. This book of Mivart was never censured.[48]

Interpretation of Genesis

In 1909 the Pontifical Biblical Commission gave a response to several questions about the interpretation of the first chapters of Genesis. In this response it maintained this cautious attitude concerning the understanding of the Scriptures and the conclusions of science. It stated that where the Fathers had different understandings of the Scriptures, exegetes were free to follow whatever interpretation they prudently judged best, as long as they respected the Church's judgment and the analogy of faith. It declared, however, that the literal and historical sense of Genesis may not be called into question as regards things pertaining to the foundations of the Christian religion, including "the special creation of man" and "the formation of the first woman from the first man," and said that the exegetical systems which sought to exclude the historical sense of the first three chapters of Genesis, and which were "defended by the pretense of science," did not have a solid foundation.[49] This restriction on the freedom of exegetes regarding interpretations of Genesis was not a doctrinal statement, but a prudential one, and it was later removed by the same Biblical Commission, which also explained that the first chapters of Genesis "relate in simple and figurative language, adapted to the understanding of mankind at a lower stage of development, the fundamental truths underlying the divine scheme of salvation," an interpretation of Genesis later taken up in the *Catechism of the Catholic Church.*[50]

The Church's response

By the mid-twentieth century, the Church was ready to speak more directly about evolution. Pope Pius XII, in *Humani Generis*, which deals mainly with evolutionism and relativism of dogma, speaks also of evolution as a scientific hypothesis. Besides expressing his judgment that science had not yet proven absolutely the origin of the human body by evolution, the pope makes three points regarding the requirements of the faith and obedience to the Church. (1) The Church allows discussion regarding the formation of the human body from living beings (by a process of evolution). (2) According to the Catholic faith, human souls are created immediately by God. (3) A Catholic must be ready to accept the teaching of the Church on the meaning of the Scriptures pertinent to man's origin, if the Church makes a pronouncement on the question.

The Pope is more strict regarding polygenism, the theory that the human race does not especially originate from one man, Adam, saying that "the faithful cannot embrace that opinion which maintains either that after Adam there existed on this earth true men who did not take their origin through natural generation from him as from the first parent of all or that Adam represents a certain number of first parents."[51] Even here, however, he does not reject the theory absolutely, but only states that one should not hold the theory, since it is not evident how it can be reconciled with the doctrine of original sin, "which proceeds from a sin actually committed by an individual Adam" and which is passed on by way of generation.[52] Many theologians have since made proposals for reconciling polygenism and original sin.[53] While their success may be debatable, and only the Church can authoritatively pronounce judgment on such proposals, the possibility of such a reconciliation effectively withdraws the prohibition against affirming polygenism. The Church therefore no longer seeks to prevent anyone from holding this position, nor does it censure them for holding it.

The Church's position at this time was basically this: the Catholic faith does not exclude the possibility of evolution, even the evolution of man, and while being cautious inasmuch as faith also has something to say about human origins, the Church is open to evidence for evolution. And as the scientific evidence for evolution continued to increase, the Church became much more favourable towards evolution.

Pope John Paul II

Pope John Paul II in a message to the Pontifical Academy of Sciences referred to Pope Pius XII's statement that evolution was a "serious hypothesis, worthy of investigation and serious study," and went on to say that "today, more than a half-century after the appearance of that encyclical, some new findings lead us toward the recognition of evolution as more than an hypothesis."[54] He refers to the convergence of independent studies in different fields. He does not mention particular examples, but one example would be the discoveries made in the field of genetics; the similarities and differences of genetic code, investigated quite independently from the studies of animal structures and the fossil record, match up with the relationships one would expect to find according to the "family tree" proposed by the theory of evolution.

Like Pius XII, Pope John Paul II makes a note about scientific methodology: we must consider the theory of evolution as it is, a scientific theory that has validity to the extent that it is verified by the facts that it is in harmony with and explains. And like Pius XII, he reminds us what our faith teaches us, namely that the human soul is from God, that man has a unique dignity, that "man is the only creature on earth that God wanted for its own sake."[55] He further explains how philosophy is a kind of mediator between scientific theory and the

Christian faith's teaching. The explanation of the theory of evolution depends upon philosophy; an explanation of evolution according to materialist philosophy, which regards the human spirit as merely the manifestation of matter, is contrary to the Christian faith regarding human dignity. A true philosophy of nature does not reduce all phenomena to matter, and can recognise an "ontological leap" between man and other animals. Such an ontological leap is not contradicted by the continuity of evolution that physics and chemistry strongly indicate. These sciences describe the *sensible manifestation* of life, which may constitute a continuum through the process of evolution, although the progress of the *fundamental natures* takes place in discrete steps.

This last point of Pope John Paul II, that the external process manifesting a fundamental development may be continuous even when that development itself is not continuous, but consists in a sudden "jump," may be illustrated by the case of a child's first rational thought, or the first moment of death. Though a baby has full human dignity and an intellect from the beginning, it is not then using its intellect and actually thinking rationally; as it matures, it begins to think rationally and act responsibly, yet we cannot point to a particular *moment* when the child has a rational thought or acts responsibly for the first time. The external manifestation of its development is continuous, though the reality revealed by it is not.

Similarly we may be able to know at some time that death has occurred, but we cannot point to the precise *moment* of death. Is it the instant the last brain wave ceases? One second later? A minute later? At some point it is clear that death has occurred, but the exact moment of death is not clear, because the physical process involved is continuous.

Similarly, Pope John Paul II understands the external and sensible manifestation of life's development to be continuous, though there were fundamental "jumps" from a lower nature to a higher nature. The essential difference between sensate and insensate[56] life does not mean that someone who was watching the process of evolution would see a sudden, inexplicable "jump" from one level of life to the next. He would most likely observe that at first the living beings clearly lacked the power of sensation, and later on clearly had it, but in between be unable to state positively whether or not the organisms were truly sensate.

In summary:

• Sacred Scripture and the faith do communicate truths about the origin of the world and about man: e.g., that the world comes from God's free and loving *plan*, that man has an *immortal soul*, which is *created by God*, and that man's broken relationship with God derives from an individual sin by our forefather.

- The question whether living beings, including men, have their historical origins in an evolutionary process, is *not* determined by the faith, and therefore the answer is to be sought through the physical sciences.

- The relation between revealed truths and the truths of natural science is to be carefully considered; the legitimate and true conclusions of natural science should be interpreted in light of a true and sound philosophy, which, since truth does not contradict truth, will always be compatible with the faith.

Compatibility of evolution and creation

In 2002 the International Theological Commission, with the approval of Cardinal Ratzinger, published the document *Communion and Stewardship*, which addressed the question of evolution. While this document is not strictly magisterial, it reflects the increasing openness of the Church to the overwhelming scientific evidence for evolution, regarding it as "virtually certain" that all living organisms have descended from some first organism.[57]

The document goes on to explain the compatibility of creation and evolution. God not only makes things in the world *be*, but makes them *be causes*. According to Catholic tradition, God, as a universal cause, "is the cause not only of existence but also the cause of causes." In creating and conserving the universe, God wills to activate the secondary causes that contribute to the natural order he intends. Through these secondary, natural causes, "God causes to arise those conditions required for the emergence and support of living organisms, and, furthermore, for their reproduction and differentiation."[58]

God is not just an extra-powerful cause, but is a *transcendent* cause. God's ability to use secondary causes to achieve the ends he intends does not do away with the proper nature and contingency of those secondary causes. "Divine causality and created causality radically differ in kind and not only in degree. Thus, even the outcome of a truly contingent natural process can nonetheless fall within God's providential plan for creation." Because the scientist's field of inquiry is limited to secondary, created causes, he may conclude quite correctly that a particular event or process resulted from chance or coincidence. Yet to conclude, further, that the process is absolutely unguided, is to make a philosophical assertion unjustified by science. "In the Catholic perspective, neo-Darwinians who adduce random genetic variation and natural selection as evidence that the process of evolution is absolutely unguided are straying beyond what can be demonstrated by science." The very contingency and randomness observed in an evolutionary process derives from God's creative action. "Any evolutionary mechanism that is contingent can only be contingent because God made it so." Hence, *no* evolutionary process can fall outside the bounds of divine providence.[59]

Complementarity of creation and evolution

Creation and evolution are not only compatible, but mutually complementary. The doctrine of creation completes the intrinsic insufficiency of the scientific account of the world, while the scientific account of evolution completes the lack of detail in the doctrine of creation.

Evolution has a twofold insufficiency, which points to and is completed by the doctrine of creation: an insufficiency on the part of the *principles* of evolution, and an insufficiency on the part of the *term*.

Evolution presupposes regular natural laws

To understand how natural principles of evolution are not sufficient unto themselves, and are dependent on God, we should first say how they are *not* insufficient. The natural principles of evolution need not be insufficient in the sense that they must be supplemented by supernatural "interventions" of God, as a designer fiddling with his creation. They *could* be insufficient in this sense, as Behe argues, but there are no solid reasons for supposing such an insufficiency. As far as we know, evolution could have occurred entirely by natural causes, that is, without "interventions" *outside* the natural order of things, such as miracles.

The philosophical principle that "nothing gives what it does not have," or that an effect cannot be greater than its causes, is sometimes used to argue that less perfect beings cannot naturally evolve into more perfect beings. The second law of thermodynamics (though not strictly applicable to this case) is sometimes used as an additional justification for this argument. Now, from this philosophical principle that an effect cannot be greater than its cause, we can legitimately conclude that the source from which all living things developed, must have been *in some way* at least as perfect as the result. But what *kind* of perfection is this? Since the historical process that the theory of evolution examines is a sequence of material development and order, the perfection in question is actually that of *matter* and its *orderliness*. The material structure of the universe must have had at the beginning just as much or more order contained potentially within it as exists actually now.

How could an "unformed" universe have within itself in a potential manner just as much order as now? At first sight this seems impossible. In fact, however, it is quite possible, and even plausible. The created material natures of things, in a context in which interaction among them occurs, are principles that have within themselves a kind of *infinite power*, just as from a few mathematical principles an *infinite number of conclusions* can be derived. We actually see many examples of this sort of thing. A seed has within itself the potential of producing a plant that has more actual structure than the seed. Water and air, under the influence of the sun's heat and the earth's motion, produce beautiful structures such as snowflakes. These examples cannot be ignored or explained away, nor are they cases of "getting something from nothing." Rather, they are examples of the way in which a few determinate principles can contain within their power much potential order, which is then actualised when there is an agent to apply these principles - in this case, a source of power, such as the sun - or circumstances in which these principles become active, such as when the seed is placed into moist earth. (If there were no source of power such as the sun, water would not actually form into rain or snowflakes, living beings would not be produced, and so on.)

If natural powers and laws are sufficient to effect evolution without being supplemented by external interventions, where does their insufficiency lie? It lies in the inability of a natural law to explain itself. Why are there natural laws in the first place? Why shouldn't everything happen entirely randomly? To explain one natural power, such as the power of water, by other natural powers, such as the powers of hydrogen and oxygen, just pushes the problem further back. It doesn't answer why nature is orderly in the first place. We can only find an answer to the ultimate question of order by looking to that which fundamentally *establishes* order, to intellect or mind - not only the human mind, which *sees* the order in nature, but does not make it, but a divine mind, which *makes* order in nature.

Arguments for/evidence of design

This argument from the fundamental and original orderliness or regularity of the universe is related to, but distinct from the argument for design based on *cosmological fine-tuning*. The argument from cosmological fine-tuning is based on two premises: (1) the values of many physical constants in nature seem to be arbitrary, in the sense that they do not follow from general theories of physics, nor can one constant be deduced from another; (2) these values have to be nearly exactly what they are in order for the world as we know it and life to be possible; if they differed more than a very tiny amount, life could not exist. Many scientists, philosophers, and theologians have argued that the precise specification of all these apparently arbitrary constants in just the manner necessary for life, including human life, is evidence of design, that is, evidence that these constants are caused by an intelligent, supernatural cause that determined these constants.

Both arguments proceed from a consideration of the physical laws of the universe. The argument from cosmological fine-tuning takes *complexity* and *precise*

58

specification of physical constants and forces as evidence for a designer of this physical world. The basis for the potential organisation of which we are speaking, on the other hand, does not consist in *complexity*, but in *order* and *regularity*. This order and regularity argues for an intelligent cause of it. Because this argument is not based on precise measurements, but on the general fact of regularity and law, it is not subject to potential revision the way that the cosmological fine-tuning argument is.

Evolution presupposes natures

Evolution of itself is not only incapable of explaining the regularity that is the principle of evolution, it is also incapable of explaining the *result* of evolution, namely *new natures*. Besides their material structure, living beings also have a real nature, and this cannot be explained through the development or evolution of material principles, except insofar as the *author of nature* made matter to be in potency to such natures, and makes the material being *to be* of such a nature. The evolution of more perfect animals from less perfect animals or even from non-living beings does not mean that they do not really have natures. Based on the likeness of activity and structure between other living beings and us, it is a matter of common sense that as we have a real and fundamental unity - we are a definite kind of thing, the kind of thing that can sense, can feel, and can move itself - so also other animals have a real unity, not simply an apparent or accidental unity.

Cause of nature

Can we still maintain this common sense notion in the face of the theory of evolution? We can. The theory of evolution in no way requires us to reject the perception that animals are a specific kind of being. Rather, the theory of evolution provides an *additional argument for the necessity of God*, who gives animals and other material beings their natures. Rather than rejecting either the immediate common sense perception or the scientific theory, we can reconcile them by recognising divine agency, which stands above all natural causes. Scientists and philosophers sometimes speak as though the need to postulate God were taken away by the fact of evolution, by the fact that higher beings are generated from lower beings. But in reality, the need for such a higher agent is even more evident in the case of an animal generating something superior to itself than in the case of an animal generating something like and equal to itself. Richard Dawkins once said that "although atheism might have been logically tenable before Darwin, Darwin made it possible to be an intellectually fulfilled atheist."[60] Dawkin's idea is that before the theory of evolution, one had no explanation other than God for the complexity of living beings. But while it is evident that living beings are *complex*, it is even more evident that they are *alive*. I am much more sure that I see, than that my eye is complex. And while evolution provides an explanation of how sight *came to be*, it provides no explanation for *sight itself*. It does not explain the simple facts of common experience: why I *see*, why I am *alive*. So even after Darwin, an atheist cannot be entirely "intellectually fulfilled," since he must steadfastly ignore the existence of nature in the world. Nature *itself*, and in particular living nature, needs a cause, *especially* if it came to be through an evolutionary process. But the cause of nature itself can only be something that transcends nature, a supernatural being.

Evolution complements the doctrine of creation

As the doctrine of creation fills out fundamental inadequacies in the theory of evolution, so the theory of evolution fills out a lack of detail in the doctrine of creation, both as regards the natural world and as regards humanity.

Evolution shows how nature has a share in producing the diversity of life that lends so much beauty to the world. We see more clearly how in both the natural and supernatural creation, God gives his creatures the nobility of *being causes*, of *sharing in his creative work*. In the Catholic understanding of justification, men and women are not only saved, but have a real share in Christ's life and in his mission of sanctification. In evolution we may see a dim analogy of this human cooperation with God's saving work. God did not simply *impose* the diversity of life on the world, but gave it the fundamental powers it needed to bring forth such a richness.

The theory of evolution, explaining the natural processes involved in human origins, can be a safeguard against possible misunderstandings of creation and the fall. Evolution precludes our thinking, for example, that the pains of childbirth or other penalties associated with original sin are positive flaws inflicted on mankind by God, rather than the withdrawal of a supernatural gift that would have preserved mankind from suffering and evil. The Catholic tradition in fact understood original sin this way long before the theory of evolution,[61] but the theory of evolution gives us a positive explanation for such bodily defects, and so makes it easier to avoid the error of thinking that they must be positively inflicted by God.

Though evolutionary psychology is still in its infancy, the theory of evolution has the potential to provide insight into human passions. E.g., if anger developed as a help for physically countering a life-threatening assailant, it would tend naturally to excess in present-day circumstances, where physical force is mostly inappropriate in solving daily problems. In this case, an evolutionary explanation would be confirming an insight already gained by spiritual masters such as St Francis de Sales, who recognise that anger can be justified, yet recommend carefully restraining it even then. But the potential also exists for evolutionary psychology to disclose knowledge about the passions that would in *detail* (though not in depth) go beyond the insights already gained through simple human experience.

Summary

Cardinal Ratzinger briefly summarises the compatibility and complementarity of creation and evolution: "We cannot say: creation *or* evolution." The story in Genesis, on the one hand, does not explain how human persons *come to be* but rather *what they are*. "It explains their inmost origin and casts light on the project that they are." The theory of evolution, on the other hand, "seeks to understand and describe biological developments." But evolution "cannot explain where the 'project' of human persons comes from, nor their inner origin, nor their particular nature." Creation and evolution show us "two complementary - rather than mutually exclusive - realities."[62]

The story of Genesis corrects possible misunderstandings of evolution, telling us that "human beings are not a mistake but something willed; they are the fruit of love."[63] It tells us that our life is not a mere blip in the history of the world, but has a meaning that transcends history. We are called to personal union with the eternal God who is the ultimate source and goal of the universe.

Conclusion

Darwin, finding that his scientific discoveries left no real room for "his" theology of creation, finally abandoned it. In intellectual and human honesty, he did not accept a "double" truth: a scientific-rational and a religious-emotional truth. His understanding of creation, however, was not that of the great Christian intellectual tradition, but was closer to that of deism and William Paley, which sees the Creator as a great "clockmaker" at the beginning of the world. Many Christians, unwittingly embracing the same understanding of creation, have rejected and still reject the scientific fact of evolution, despite the overwhelming evidence for it.

In the great Christian tradition of creation, however, evolution does not make the postulate of God the Creator an unnecessary "hypothesis," but discloses the most *intimate* manner in which God the Creator is active within creation, bringing forth one being from another being, one species from another species. Christianity has nothing to fear from evolution, but may indeed welcome it, insofar as evolution reveals new details about God's creation and about man. Conversely, if scientists, proponents, and followers of Darwin do not neglect

Christianity's impulse to look beyond the scientific method, to ask the deeper questions about the ultimate origin and goal of life, they will in turn profit from this engagement with theology and philosophy.

The history of the relationship between evolution and creation is a complicated one. Misunderstandings have occurred and still occur on both sides. Evolutionists have claimed to answer the ultimate questions about man's origin and destiny, declaring that human life is a mere happenstance, fleeting and ultimately meaningless. Creationists, in turn, have claimed to answer the very particular questions about man's and the biological world's exact historical origins. Both sides have at times gone too far in the assertions made on the basis of their legitimate insights. It is our hope that this book will contribute to a better understanding of the right relationship between the theory of evolution and the doctrine of creation, a relationship that is beneficial both to the scientist and to the believer.

Further Reading

Intelligent Design

William A. Dembski and Sean McDowell. *Understanding Intelligent Design*. Eugene, Oregon: Harvest House, 2008.

Tkacz, Michael W. *Thomas Aquinas Vs. the Intelligent Designers: What is God's Finger Doing in My Pre-Biotic Soup?* 9th September, 2005. *http://guweb2.gonzaga.edu/faculty/calhoun/socratic/Tkacz_AquinasvsID.html*. (A philosophical critique of Intelligent Design Theory from a Thomistic perspective.)

Theory and Evidence for Evolution

Denis Alexander. *Creation or Evolution: Do We Have to Choose?* Oxford: Monarch Books, 2008.

Jerry Coyne. *Why Evolution is True*. New York: Viking Adult, 2009.

Douglas J. Futuyma. *Evolutionary Biology*, 3rd ed. Sunderland, MA: Sinauer Associates, 1997.

Non-darwinian Scientific Theories of Evolution

Jean Staune, *Darwinism Design and Purpose: A European Perspective*. Paper presented at *Science and Religion: Global Perspectives*, Philadelphia, Penn. 4th-8th June, 2005.

http://www.metanexus.net/conference2005/pdf/staune.pdf

66

Creation and Evolution

William E. Carroll, *Creation, Evolution, and Thomas Aquinas*, *Revue des Questions Scientifiques* 171.4 (2000): 319-347. *http://www.catholiceducation.org/articles/science/sc0035.html.*

Christoph Schönborn, *Chance or Purpose?: Creation, Evolution, and a Rational Faith.* Edited by Hubert Philip Weber. Translated by Henry Taylor. San Francisco: Ignatius Press, 2007.

International Theological Commission. *Communion and Stewardship. http://www.vatican.va/roman_curia/congregations /cfaith/cti_documents/rc_con_cfaith_doc_20040723_communio n-stewardship_en.html.*

Endnotes

[1] John Hedley Brooke, "Revisiting Darwin on Order and Design," in *Design and Disorder: Perspectives from Science and Theology*, ed. Niels Henrik Gregersen and Ulf Görman (London: T&T Clark, 2002), 39–41.

[2] Don O'Leary, *Roman Catholicism and Modern Science: A History* (New York: Continuum, 2007), 28–29.

[3] While the personal motivation in some cases may not be a religious motive, and the arguments for intelligent design are not *essentially* religious, the movement itself has roots in religious faith.

[4] Christoph Schönborn, *Chance or Purpose?: Creation, Evolution, and a Rational Faith*, ed. Hubert Philip Weber, trans. Henry Taylor (San Francisco: Ignatius Press, 2007).

[5] Robert Sungenis, "Dialogue on Evolution versus Creationism," Catholic Apologetics International, http://www.catholicintl.com/scienceissues/dialogue-evolution-print.htm (accessed 9th June, 2009).

[6] *Ibid.*

[7] See Meredith G. Kline, "Because it had not rained," *Westminster Theological Journal* 20 (1958):146–157, for a detailed exposition of this argument.

[8] John C. Avise, *Adaption and Complex Design* (Washington, DC: National Academies Press, 2007), 298, citing Buell's preface to the third edition of *Of Pandas and People*.

[9] *Ibid.*, 299–300.

[10] Michael J. Behe, "From Muttering to Mayhem: How Phillip Johnson Got Me Moving" in *Darwin's Nemesis*, ed. William A. Dembski, 42.

[11] *Ibid.*, 44.

[12] Behe, *Darwin's Black Box: The Biochemical Challenge to Evolution* (New York: The Free Press, 1996).

[13] Charles Darwin, *On the Origin of Species*, ch. 6.

[14] *Darwin's Black Box*, 232–233.

[15] See, for example, Kenneth Miller, *Finding Darwin's God: A Scientist's Search for Common Ground Between God and Evolution* (New York: Harper Perennial, 2000), 134–158.

[16] Dawkins, *The Blind Watchmaker* (New York: W.W. Norton & Co., 1986), 9.

[17] Clive Davidson, "Creatures from primordial silicon," *New Scientist* 156, no. 2108 (15th November, 1997):30–35.

[18] Dembski addresses a genetic algorithm that learned to play checkers at the expert level, arguing that the information was inserted from the beginning, that the programs were "guided," because the programmers "kept the criterion of winning constant" (*No Free Lunch*, 2nd edition [Lanham, MD: Rowman & Littlefield, 2007], 223). But while keeping "the criterion of winning constant" may be part of the *regularity* such an algorithm presupposes, there is nothing more natural than that the "criterion of winning" in checkers should remain constant, and does not indicate any design of the *solution* to the problem by the programmers.

[19] See, for example, Dembski, *Intelligent Design: The Bridge Between Science & Theology* (Downers Grove, IL: InterVarsity Press, 2002), 177, and *No Free Lunch*, 287 ff. Though Dembski relies on the argument from irreducible complexity, it is not clear whether he perceived its strict *necessity* for the validity of his argument.

[20] Michael Behe, *Darwin's Black Box*, 176.

[21] Michael Behe, "Reply to My Critics," *Biology and Philosophy* 16 (2001):685–709, 697.

[22] Michael Behe, *Darwin's Black Box*, 29, citing H. Allen Orr and Jerry A. Coyne, "The Genetics of Adaptation: A Reassessment," *The American Naturalist* 140 (1992):726.

[23] Jerry Coyne, "More Crank Science," *Boston Review* (February/March 1997).

[24] *Ibid.*

[25] Cardinal Schönborn, lecture at the Austrian Academy of Sciences on 4th March, 2009, Katholische Nachrichten, *http://www.kath.net/detail.php?id=22299*. Accessed 9th June, 2009.

[26] Origen, *The Fundamental Doctrines* 4:1:16.

[27] St Justin, *Dialog with Typho the Jew*, ch. 81; Irenaeus, *Against Heresies*, 5:23.

[28] Hugh Ross and Gleason L. Archer, "The Day-age view," in *The Genesis Debate: Three Views on the Days of Creation*, ed. David G. Hogopian (Mission Viejo, CA: Crux Press, 2001).

[29] Theophilus, *To Autolycus* 2:15.

[30] St Augustine, *City of God*, 11:7; *Literal Interpretation of Genesis*, 2:14, 4:21–26.

[31] St Augustine, *The Literal Interpretation of Genesis* 6:5–8; 4:33, 52; 5:4–14; *Questions on the Heptateuch*, 2:21.

[32] St Augustine, *The Literal Interpretation of Genesis* 1:19–20.

[33] *Ibid.*, 2:9.

[34] *Summa Theologiae* I, q. 45, a. 1.

[35] *Summa Theologiae* I, q. 22, a. 2 ad 1.

[36] Lateran IV, "Confession of Faith"; Vatican I, "Canons on God the Creator", 5.

[37] *Catechism of the Catholic Church* (CCC) 301.

[38] CCC 308.

[39] CCC 366.

[40] Douglas J. Futuyma, *Evolutionary Biology*, 2nd ed. (Sunderland, MA: Sinauer Associates, 1986), 15.

[41] Jerry Coyne gives a popular overview of the evidence for evolution in *Why Evolution is True* (New York: Viking Adult, 2009). A more technical overview by Douglas Theobald, *29+ Evidences for Macroevolution: The Scientific Case for Common Descent*, may be found at *http://www.talkorigins.org/faqs/comdesc/*.

[42] International Theological Commission, *Communion and Stewardship*, n. 62.

[43] *Philosophical Notebook*, note made on 9th Dec, 1863.

[44] Mariano Artigas, Thomas F. Glick, and Rafael A. Martinez, *Negotiating Darwin: The Vatican Confronts Evolution 1877–1902* (Baltimore: John Hopkins University Press), 248, 276.

[45] *Ibid.*, 29.

[46] Brian W. Harrison, in an article on this subject, "Early Vatican Responses to Evolutionist Theology," *Living Tradition*, no. 93 (May 2001), neglects to properly distinguish the Congregation of the Index from the Holy Office, attributing the Congregation's decisions to the Holy Office itself.

[47] *Negotiating Darwin*, 16, 30.

[48] *Negotiating Darwin*, 239.

[49] "Response of the Pontifical Biblical Commission on the historical character of the first three chapters of Genesis," *Enchiridion Biblicum* 324–331. AAS 1 (1909), 567–569.

[50] "Letter of the Pontifical Biblical Commission to Cardinal Suhard," 16th January, 1948. *Enchiridion Biblicum* 577–563. AAS 40 (1949), 45–48. Cf. *Catechism of the Catholic Church* 337.

[51] Pope Pius XII, *Humani Generis*, n. 37.

[52] *Ibid.*

[53] See, e.g., Jerry D. Korsmeyer, *Evolution and Eden: Balancing Original Sin and Contemporary Science* (Mahwah, NJ: Paulist Press, 1988); Daryl P. Domning and Monika Hellwig, *Original selfishness: original sin and evil in the light of*

evolution (Burlington, VT: Ashgate Publishing, 2006). A brief summary of several hypotheses is given by Roberto Masi, in "The Credo of Paul VI: Theology of Original Sin and the Scientific Theory of Evolution," *L'Osservatore Romano*, 17th April 1969.

[54] Pope John Paul II, *Message to the Pontifical Academy of Sciences*, 22nd October 1996, n. 4.

[55] *Ibid.*, n. 5.

[56] "Sensate" and "insensate" correspond roughly to the common notion of "animal" and "plant," but we use these more abstract terms in order to avoid confusion with the use of "animal" and "plant" in biology.

[57] International Theological Commission, *Communion and Stewardship*, n. 63.

[58] *Ibid.*

[59] *Ibid.*

[60] *The Blind Watchmaker*, page 6.

[61] St Thomas Aquinas explained that fallen nature is metaphysically the state of pure human nature, called *fallen* only by comparison with the gratuitous gift of original justice (In *II Sent.*, d. 30, a. 1, ad 3, *Summa Theologiae* I, q. 85, a. 1).

[62] Cardinal Joseph Ratzinger, *In the Beginning* (Grand Rapids, MI: Eerdmans, 1995), 50.

[63] *Ibid.*, 57.

Global Warming
How should we respond?

Global warming is seen by many as the defining issue of our generation. Does the Church believe that it is really happening? What should Catholics do to care for our planet? This booklet looks at the science and the theology of the problem, and in the light of Catholic social teaching, proposes a response which gives humanity a privileged place in creation but also a special responsibility towards the planet and towards other human beings created by God.

Russell Sparkes was born into the Catholic Faith in 1955. His other books include *Prophet of Orthodoxy - the Wisdom of G.K. Chesterton*, and *Sound of Heaven, an Anthology of Catholic Poetry*. He is a member of The Keys, the Catholic Writers' Guild.

ISBN: 978 1 86082 554 5

CTS Code: Ex 30